Written by Amanda Cant

Illustrated by David Lock

A popular sport

Football is a very popular sport. Every day, somewhere in the world children are playing football together.

Children play football on the beach, in the city, in the park and at school.

Lots of children want to be professional football players. In some countries there are professional football teams for women.

Do women play professional football in your country?

Football heroes

Football has many heroes and famous players. Can you see your favourite player here?

This is Fernando Torres. He's from Spain. He scores lots of goals.

This is Wayne Rooney. He's from England. He plays for Manchester United.

This is Ronaldinho.
He's from Brazil.
He can run fast.

This is Francesco Totti.
He's from Italy. He's
kicking the ball.

The World Cup

The World Cup competition happens every four years. Football fans all over the world watch the World Cup on TV.

This family want England to win.

Italy are the World Cup 2006 winners. Fabio Cannavaro is holding the World Cup trophy. It is made of gold and is 48 centimetres high. The team are really happy.

Football fans

Lots of fans are football crazy. They want everyone to know which team they support.

They wave flags and football scarves. They wear wigs and they paint their faces. They play music and they sing football songs.

Sometimes fans are happy and sometimes they're very sad.

Everyone wants their team to win!

Children love football!

Children who play football run.

They throw the ball.

They kick the ball.

They jump in the air.

They play together in a team.

What a Goal!

Written by Amanda Cant

Illustrated by David Lock

This is Felix and Nina. Felix is ten and Nina is nine. They're brother and sister. Nina gets ready to play football. She's football crazy!

Look at Nina's football posters and her football clothes. Look at her toys.

Felix gets ready to play football. He's football crazy, too!

Look at Felix's football books and comics.
Look at his school bag and pencil case.

They play football together every day. They play in the summer when it's hot and sunny.

They play in the autumn when it's raining.

They play in the winter when it's snowing.

They play football with their friends at school.

They play football in the park.

They play football with friends on the beach.

In August, Nina and Felix go on holiday with their mum and dad. They're camping at the seaside. It's sunny and they're getting ready to go to the beach.

At ten o'clock, Mum, Dad, Nina and Felix are at the beach. Mum and Dad are reading their books. Nina and Felix are playing football. They're making new friends.

Lots of children are playing football together. It's a great game and everybody's happy. Felix is playing really well. But suddenly ...

Felix is taking the penalty. Everybody's watching and shouting. Nina's in goal. She's scared.

Her legs are shaking.
Her arms are shaking.
She closes her eyes ...

... and she misses the ball! It's a goal!

Nina leaves the football game and goes back to the campsite with her dad.

Nina goes back to the beach and the football game.

Felix passes the ball to Nina. She runs fast.

She turns right. She runs past the tall boy.

She turns left. She runs past the short boy.

Now it's just Nina and the boy in goal. Nina looks at the goal. She kicks the ball and she scores a goal!

Nina's team are really happy. Nina jumps in the air. Her cap falls off.

Activities

1 Read and colour.

This girl is football crazy. She's wearing a red wig. Her face is green and blue. Her scarf is green and red. Her T-shirt is red. Her shorts are green. Her socks are green and blue. Her trainers are white.

This boy is football crazy. He's wearing a green and yellow wig. His face is blue and red. His T-shirt is blue. His shorts are red. His socks are yellow. His trainers are blue.

2 Circle T (True) or F (False).

1 Felix and Nina are brother and sister. (T) F
2 The family go on holiday in September. T F
3 They go camping in the mountains. T F
4 Girls can play football. T F
5 Felix is nine years old. T F
6 Felix and Nina play football every day. T F

3 Draw and write about a football player. Choose your favourite or make one up.

His name is ______________.

He's from ______________.

His hair is ______________.

His shirt is ______________.

His shorts are ______________.

4 Match the sentences to the pictures.

1 They play football in the summer when it's sunny.

2 They play football in the autumn when it's raining.

3 They play football in the winter when it's snowing.

4 They play football in the spring when it's windy.

5 Write the actions.

~~kicking~~ running turning left turning right throwing jumping

1 kicking ________ 2 ________ 3 ________

4 ________ 5 ________ 6 ________

6 Tick the answers. Then check and count your goals.

1 This footballer is very:

- happy. ☑
- sad. ☐
- scared. ☐

2 The World Cup competition is every:

- two years. ☐
- three years. ☐
- four years. ☐

3 This is the flag for:

- Portugal. ☐
- France. ☐
- Italy. ☐

4 The World Cup trophy is:

- 28 centimetres high. ☐
- 38 centimetres high. ☐
- 48 centimetres high. ☐

5 Ronaldinho is from:

- Australia. ☐
- Brazil. ☐
- Italy. ☐

6 This is the flag for:

- France. ☐
- England. ☐
- Brazil. ☐

7 The World Cup 2006 winners are:

- France. ☐
- Spain. ☐
- Italy. ☐

Answers: Count your goals!

1 happy. ●
2 four years. ○
3 Italy. ○
4 48 centimetres high. ○
5 Brazil. ○
6 England. ○
7 Italy. ○

Picture Dictionary

bedroom
poster
toy
comic
school bag
pencil case
seaside
shorts
winter
spring
summer
autumn
trainers
camping
penalty
goal

Macmillan Education
4 Crinan Street
London N1 9XW
A division of Macmillan Publishers Limited
Companies and representatives throughout the world

ISBN 978 0 2300 1017 8
ISBN 978 0 2300 1016 1 (International Edition)

First published 2007

Illustrated by David Lock
Designed by Red Giraffe Limited

The author and publishers would like to thank the following
for permission to reproduce their photographic material:

Cover Photography with the kind permission of Alamy/vario images
GmbH & Co. KG

ActionPlus/ Neil Tingle pp4(l), 7,8 and 9; Alamy/ Kolvenbach p1,
Alamy/ Ian Miles-Flashpoint Pictures p6; Getty Images/ Ty Allison p2,
Getty/ Julian Finney p3, Getty/ Stuart Franklin p5(l),
Getty/ Patrik Stollarz p5(r); Rex Features p4(r).

Printed and bound in Uruguay

2023
22